ROALD DAHL

Penguin

THE WITCHES

Illustrated by Quentin Blake

LEVEL

4

This book has been simplified for English Language Learners

LB of Hackney

91300001198628

PENGUIN BOOKS

UK | USA | Canada | Ireland | Australia
India | New Zealand | South Africa

Penguin Books is part of the Penguin Random House group of companies
whose addresses can be found at global.penguinrandomhouse.com.

www.penguin.co.uk   www.puffin.co.uk   www.ladybird.co.uk

Penguin
Random House
UK

The Witches first published in Great Britain by Jonathan Cape
and in the USA by Farrar, Straus and Giroux 1983
Published by Puffin Books 1985
Reissued 2016, 2022
This Penguin Readers edition published by Penguin Books Ltd, 2024
001

Original text written by Roald Dahl
Text for Penguin Readers edition adapted by Karen Kovacs
Text copyright © The Roald Dahl Story Company Ltd, 1983
Illustrations copyright © Quentin Blake, 1983
Additional illustrations (pages 6, 20, 36, 66, 80) and reworked illustrations
by Laura Coppolaro for The Roald Dahl Story Company

Copyright © The Roald Dahl Story Company Ltd / Quentin Blake, 2024.
ROALD DAHL is a registered trademark of The Roald Dahl Story Company Ltd.

The moral right of Roald Dahl and Quentin Blake has been asserted

Printed and bound in Great Britain by Clays Ltd, Elcograf S.p.A.

The authorized representative in the EEA is Penguin Random House Ireland,
Morrison Chambers, 32 Nassau Street, Dublin D02 YH68.

A CIP catalogue record for this book is available from the British Library

ISBN: 978-0-241-61114-2

All correspondence to:
Penguin Books
Penguin Random House Children's
One Embassy Gardens, 8 Viaduct Gardens, London SW11 7BW

MIX
Paper | Supporting
responsible forestry
FSC
www.fsc.org   FSC® C018179

Penguin Random House is committed to a
sustainable future for our business, our readers
and our planet. This book is made from Forest
Stewardship Council® certified paper.

CONTENTS

ABOUT ROALD DAHL AND QUENTIN BLAKE

 Roald Dahl was a children's writer, and many of his stories are very famous across the world. Do you know any Roald Dahl books?

 Quentin Blake drew pictures for Roald Dahl's stories. Do you like the pictures in this book? Which is your favourite picture?

About this story

Roald Dahl was born in the UK, but his parents were from Norway. When he was a child, Dahl spent many happy summer holidays in Norway, where his grandparents still lived. The boy in this story is also Norwegian, but goes to school in England.

Dahl's mother told him stories from Norway. Many countries, like Norway, have frightening stories about witches. Roald Dahl wrote this story about witches, and it is frightening because the witches hate children and try to catch them.

MEET . . .

Me!

Grandma

The Grand High Witch

The Witches

Bruno Jenkins

Chapter 1 and Chapter 2
NEW WORDS

get *(got)* rid of (v.)

make something go away

disappear (v.)

A person was here, but suddenly you cannot see them.

recognize (v.)

know who someone is

a glove (n.)

You wear *gloves* on your hands.

a claw (n.)

A cat has *claws* on its feet. They can hurt you.

bald (adj.)

A *bald* person has no hair on their head.

a wig (n.)

A *wig* looks like hair. But it is not real.

poo (n.)

You do a *poo* in the toilet.

Chapter 1 and Chapter 2
WHAT DO YOU THINK?

What will happen in the story?
Answer the questions.

1   Look at the picture on page 9.
Can you see the witch?
What does the witch want to do?

2   Look at the picture on page 11.
Who are these people?
How are they feeling?

3   Look at the picture on page 17.
How are a witch's feet different?

Now let's read Chapter 1 and Chapter 2!

CHAPTER 1
Witches

In stories, witches always wear black hats and have black cats. But I am not telling you a story. I am going to tell you about *real* witches. Listen very carefully, and never forget what I am going to tell you.

Real witches wear normal clothes. They live in normal houses and do normal jobs. That is why it is so hard to catch them.

A real witch hates children. A real witch wants to **get rid of** all children. She thinks about nothing else. Even when she is working or in a shop or driving around in an expensive car, she is always thinking to herself, *Which child shall I get rid of next?* A witch enjoys getting rid of children the same way that *you* enjoy eating chocolate.

To feel happy, a witch must get rid of one child a week. That is fifty-two children a year. Very carefully, the witch chooses a child to catch. Then the witch follows that child, moving slowly and quietly, like a cat watching a little bird in the forest.

The witch gets closer and closer. Then, when she gets to the child, there is fire, animals scream, skin burns, and the child **disappears**.

A witch does not use a gun or a knife. People who do those things are caught by the police. But a witch is very clever, and she is never caught.

For children, a witch is the most dangerous thing in the world. You will soon find out that a witch does not always *look* dangerous. And, of course, this means that you have to be very careful! I am going to tell you about all their secrets. But even when you know these, you can never be sure if a woman is a witch or just a kind woman.

Please study this picture below. Which woman is the witch? That is a difficult question, but it is a question that every child must try to answer.

A witch might live near your home. Or maybe she sat next to you on the bus this morning. Or she might be the woman with the beautiful smile who gave you a sweet in the street.

She might even be your lovely schoolteacher, who is reading you these words. Look carefully at that teacher. Maybe she is smiling and saying, "Don't be silly! How could I be a witch?" But do not forget that witches are clever. Maybe your teacher is not a witch, but it is *possible*.

We are lucky, because there are not many real witches in the world today. But you should still be worried. In England, there are about a hundred of them in total. Some countries have more witches, others have fewer. Every country has some witches.

My grandmother was Norwegian. People know all about witches in her country because Norway, with its dark forests and icy mountains, is where the first witches came from. My father and mother were also Norwegian, but I lived in England with them. Twice a year, we went to visit my grandmother in Norway. I loved her very much and we were very close.

Soon after my seventh birthday, my parents took me to Norway to have Christmas with my grandmother, like we did every year. One day, while my father and mother and I were driving in icy weather, our car went off the road and down the side of a mountain. My parents were killed, but I only had a cut on my head.

I cannot talk about that terrible afternoon. I still feel very sad when I think about it. After the accident, I went to my grandmother's house and, with her arms around me, we both cried all night.

"What are we going to do now?" I asked.

"You'll stay here with me," she said. "I'll look after you."

"Aren't we going back to England?"

"No," she said. "I can't ever do that. I love Norway too much."

The next day, to stop me thinking about the accident, my grandmother started to tell me stories. She was a wonderful storyteller, but her best stories were the ones about witches. She knew a lot about them.

"These stories are true," she told me. "Everything that I'm telling you actually happened. Witches are all around us and you must believe that."

"Are the stories *really* true, Grandma?"

"Yes, they are," she said. "My dear, you won't live to be as old as me if you can't **recognize** a witch. Listen to me and remember everything that I tell you."

We were in the living room of her house in Norway, and I was ready for bed. It was snowing outside. I sat on the floor by her feet and looked up at her.

"I know children who disappeared and were never seen again," she said. "The witches took them."

"You're just trying to make me afraid," I said.

"No, I want you to be safe," she said. "I love you and I want you to stay with me."

"Tell me about the children who disappeared," I said.

"One child was called Ranghild. She was playing with her little sister in the garden. When their mother came outside, she asked, *Where's Ranghild?*

She went away with the tall woman, the sister said.

What tall woman? the mother asked.

*The woman in the white **gloves***, the sister said."

My grandmother continued, "Everyone in the town helped look for her."

"Didn't they find her?" I asked.

"No one ever saw Ranghild again," she replied. "The story of another child was very strange," my grandmother continued. "There was a family called Christiansen, and they had a big, old painting in the living room. The painting showed some ducks and a farmhouse, but there were no people in it. One day, their daughter Solveg came home from school, eating an apple. *A nice woman gave this apple to me*, Solveg said.

"The next morning, little Solveg was not in her bed. Her parents looked for her everywhere, but they couldn't find her. Then, suddenly, her father shouted, *There she is! That's Solveg! She's feeding the ducks!* He was pointing at the painting and he was right. Solveg was in the painting. The father ran closer to the painting and touched her. But she was now part of the painting."

"Did you ever see that painting with the little girl in it, Grandma?"

"Many times," my grandmother said. "Solveg kept moving around in the picture. One day, she was inside the farmhouse. Another day, she was outside holding a duck. Then one day, she just disappeared."

"Where did she go?" I asked.

"Nobody knows," my grandmother said.

"What happened to the other children?"

"They disappeared, too," my grandmother answered. "Every time, a strange woman was seen outside the house just before it happened. But that's enough for tonight. Now it's time for you to go to bed."

"I hope that a witch won't come in through my window in the night," I said, quietly.

"No," my grandmother said. "A witch will never do something silly like that. You'll be safe in your bed. Goodnight."

CHAPTER 2
How to recognize a witch

The next evening, after my bath, my grandmother told me another story about witches.

"Tonight," the old woman said, "I'm going to tell you how to recognize a real witch when you see one."

"Don't they look the same as us, Grandma?"

"Yes, they do," my grandmother replied, "and that's the problem. But there are some things that you can look for. First, a witch always wears gloves."

"But not always, of course. A witch doesn't wear gloves when it's hot," I said.

"She wears gloves even in the summer, and even in the house," my grandmother said. "And do you know why?"

"Why?" I asked.

"She has **claws** like a cat and doesn't want anyone to see them. But lots of women wear gloves, so that doesn't help you much. The second thing to remember is that a real witch has no hair."

"Is she **bald**?" I asked.

"She's as bald as an egg," my grandmother replied. "But she always wears a **wig**."

"That's no problem!" I said, happily. "I'll pull her hair and see if it's a wig."

"You can't do that!" my grandmother cried. "Some people wear a wig, but they're not witches!"

"So that doesn't help me much either," I said, sadly.

"Maybe not, but the wigs are a big problem for witches," my grandmother said. "They're very hot and uncomfortable!"

"How do you know all this, Grandma?" I asked. My grandmother did not reply.

"Witches have very large nose holes," she continued.

"Why?" I asked.

"The bigger holes help witches to smell children, and then they can catch them! A real witch can smell a child who is standing on the other side of the street on a *dark night*."

"She couldn't smell *me*," I said. "I've just had a bath."

"Oh yes, she could," my grandmother said. "Witches hate the smell of children. To a witch, children smell like dog's **poo** and it makes her sick. And when you're clean, you smell worse. When you haven't washed for a week, and you're really dirty, she can't smell you very well."

"I'll never have a bath again," I said.

"Just don't have a bath too often," my grandmother said.

"Once a month is enough for a child."

Now I loved my grandmother even more!

"What else should I look for?" I asked.

"Look carefully at the eyes," my grandmother continued, "because the eyes of a real witch are different from yours and mine. The bit in the middle isn't black. It keeps changing colour. You'll see fire and you'll see ice, dancing in her eyes."

"Is that all that is different?" I asked.

"There's one more thing," she said. "And that's their feet. Witches have square feet."

"Square feet! They don't have square feet!" I cried. "Is walking difficult for them?"

"No," my grandmother answered, "but normal shoes are very uncomfortable."

"But if a witch is wearing shoes, it won't help me to recognize her!"

"That's true. You can never be sure that a woman is a witch just by looking at her," my grandmother continued. "But if she's wearing gloves and has hair that might be a wig, and if she has uncomfortable shoes and large nose holes and strange eyes – if she has all of these things, RUN AWAY!"

Chapter 1 and Chapter 2
WHAT CAN YOU REMEMBER?

What do these words mean?

1	recognize	A person was here, but suddenly you cannot see them.
2	get rid of	know who someone is
3	poo	having no hair on your head
4	a claw	You do this in the toilet.
5	a wig	This looks like hair. But it is not real.
6	disappear	make something go away
7	a glove	You wear these on your hands.
8	bald	A cat has these on its feet. They can hurt you.

Answer the questions.

1 What do witches want to get rid of?

They want to get rid of all children.

2 How many witches are there in England?

_____

3 Where do Solveg's family find her, after she disappears?

_____

4 What do witches wear?

_____

5 Why doesn't the boy want to have a bath?

_____

6 What is different about witches' eyes?

_____

Chapter 3 and Chapter 4
NEW WORDS

a potion (n.)

a special drink that
witches make

turn into (v.)

become something different

a screen (n.)

a large flat thing.
No one can see you behind it.

a manager (n.)

an important person
in a business

escape (v.)

run away from a bad
place or person

lock (v.)

close a door with a key

a mask (n.)

You wear a *mask*
over your face.

a mousetrap (n.)

A *mousetrap* kills mice.

Chapter 3 and Chapter 4
WHAT DO YOU THINK?

What will happen next in the story?
Answer the questions.

1   Look at the picture on page 24.
   What is in the woman's hand?

2   Look at the picture on page 26.
   Why is Grandma in bed?

3   Look at the picture on page 29.
   What is this woman wearing on her hands?
   Does she look friendly?

Now let's read Chapter 3 and Chapter 4!

CHAPTER 3
Summer holidays

The next day, my grandmother said to me, "I've received a letter from your parents' lawyer, asking me to look after you."

I was pleased to hear that.

"But," she continued, "your parents wanted you to go to school in England."

"Oh, Grandma!" I cried. "You don't want us to move to England, do you?"

"Of course I don't," she answered. "But we must, and school starts again soon."

So the next day, my grandmother started making plans to move to England.

On the evening before we left for England, my grandmother began talking about her favourite topic.

"There are fewer witches in England than in Norway," she said.

"That's good," I said.

"But they are the worst witches in the world," my grandmother added.

"What do they do?" I asked.

"They make **potions**. Then they give them to children and the children **turn into** animals. Often it's a small animal. And then an adult steps on it and kills it, without knowing that it's a child."

"That's terrible!" I cried. "I really don't want to go back to England now, Grandma."

"I don't want to go either," she answered. "But we have to go."

"Does every country have witches?" I asked.

"Yes," she replied. "And once a year, all the witches in one country have a big, secret meeting. It is often in a hotel and, at the meeting, The Grand High Witch speaks to them."

"Who's that?" I asked.

"She's the most important witch in the world," my grandmother said. "And she's horrible. All the other witches are afraid of her. She travels from country to country, going to the secret meetings."

"Where does The Grand High Witch live?" I asked.

"Nobody knows," my grandmother replied, "but many people have tried to find her."

The next morning, we went to my parents' house in England. I started school again and everything seemed normal.

At the bottom of our garden, there was an enormous tree. One Saturday afternoon, I decided to start building a treehouse in it. It was spring, and being high up in the tree was lovely, with the young green leaves all around me. I was working very hard when, suddenly, I saw a woman standing below me. She was looking up at me with a strange smile on her face.

Why was this strange woman in our garden? I noticed that she was wearing a small black hat and long black gloves. *Gloves!* She was wearing *gloves!* I could not move because I was so afraid.

"I have a present for you," she said, still looking at me and smiling.

I did not answer.

"Come down from that tree, little boy," she said, "and I'll give you the most exciting present that you've ever had."

She took a bright green snake from her bag and said, "Look, here's a snake. If you come down, I'll give it to you."

Oh, Grandma, I thought, *come and help me!*

Now I climbed as high as I could in the tree and stayed there, shaking. I could not see the woman now. I stayed up there for hours and did not move. It started to get dark, and then, finally, I heard my grandmother calling me.

"Grandma!" I shouted back. "I'm up here! Has that woman gone?"

"What woman?" she asked.

"The woman with the black gloves."

My grandmother was silent. Then she said, "Yes, my dear, she's gone. You can come down now."

I came down and she put her arms around me.

"I've seen a witch," I said.

We went inside and I told my grandmother everything. When I finished, her face was grey and she was shaking, too.

I never saw that woman again. That was my first witch. But it was not my last.

The school year passed and soon it was the summer holidays. But the holidays did not start well because my grandmother became very ill. A nurse lived in our house and looked after her. I was very worried about her, but I was not allowed to go into her bedroom. After about ten days, the nurse finally said, "You can see your grandmother now." So I ran in and put my arms around her.

25

"I'll be all right," she said. "Don't worry."

My grandmother wanted to go to Norway on holiday, but the doctor told her, "No, you've been very ill. That journey would be too long for you."

So we decided to go to Bournemouth, in England, and stay in the Hotel Magnificent.

The Hotel Magnificent was an enormous white building by the sea, and it looked like a boring place for a summer holiday.

I had my own room, but it had a door to my grandmother's room. I took my two white mice with me. They were a present from my grandmother, and I called them William and Mary.

I soon found a large, empty hall with two very big doors. In front of the doors, there was a sign, which said:

26

Do not come in. This hall is for a private meeting.

The doors were open, and nobody was there, so I went inside. *I'm sure that the people from the meeting have all gone home*, I thought. *This is a lovely secret place to play with my mice.*

I went to the back of the hall, behind a **screen**, and I started playing with William and Mary.

Nobody will be able to see me here, I thought, happily.

Suddenly, I heard voices. I was worried because I could hear the hotel **manager**, Mr Stringer.

"Here's the hall for your meeting," he was saying. "Come and have tea with me after your meeting!" Looking through the screen, I could see a large group of women coming in through the doors.

27

CHAPTER 4
The meeting

Soon the hall was full of about a hundred women. They wore pretty clothes and all of them had hats. They all looked kind and friendly, and I decided to stay and continue playing with my mice.

After a little while, I looked through the screen again, and I noticed that one woman kept touching her hair. She looked hot and uncomfortable. It was a hot day, but she was wearing gloves. Then I looked around the hall, and I noticed that all the women were wearing gloves!

I felt very cold and I began to shake. I wanted to run! But I could not **escape** because the doors were already closed, and a woman was **locking** them.

I must stay quiet, I thought. *If I make one sound, a hundred witches will catch me!*

Suddenly, the witches were quiet. They seemed excited but also very afraid. A woman was standing at the front of the room. She was very small, quite young and very pretty. She was wearing gloves, but she did not look like a witch.

Then, very slowly, the young woman put her hands to her face. She took off her pretty face and she now held it in her hands. It was not her real face! It was a **mask**, and her real face was horrible.

Her eyes were like snake's eyes, and now I knew that this was The Grand High Witch.

"Take off your gloves!" she told the witches. They took off their gloves, and I saw that they all had claws.

"Take off your shoes!" she shouted. And I saw that they all had square feet.

"Take off your wigs!" cried The Grand High Witch. And I saw their bald heads.

Oh, help! I thought. *I'm in a room with a hundred horrible child-killers and the doors are locked! I can't escape!*

Then I remembered witches' nose holes. With their special nose holes, witches could smell a child on a dark night from the other side of the street. *They're going to smell me!* I thought, and I was very worried now.

I looked at my hands and they were very dirty. *I haven't had a bath for a long time,* I thought. *Maybe they won't be able to smell me.*

The Grand High Witch began to speak. "Witches of England!" she shouted. "What's the matter with you?"

The witches began to shake.

"I was having my breakfast this morning, and what did I see?" The Grand High Witch continued. "Hundreds of children were playing on the beach. Ugly little children! Why haven't you got rid of them?"

Nobody answered her.

"Children smell! Children are horrible! We don't want any children in this world!" she said.

All the witches nodded.

"Before I come back next year," she said, "you must KILL them all!"

The witches were surprised. "How can we do that?" a few of them cried.

"Shut up, all of you!" The Grand High Witch shouted. "You're all stupid, so I'll tell you what to do. I have made a potion that will turn children into mice!"

The witches were excited. And they smiled horrible smiles and shouted, "You're so clever!"

"Shut up and listen!" shouted The Grand High Witch. "This is my plan. Each of you must go home and open a new sweet shop."

"Yes, yes!" the witches cried.

The Grand High Witch continued, "You will tell all the horrible children in your town, *Today is a special day.*

You can have sweets from my shop and they're free! And all the children will come to your shop."

"Yes, yes!" the witches shouted.

"But every sweet will have some potion in it," said The Grand High Witch. "And what does the potion do? It turns children into mice!"

"Oh yes! Mice!" cried the witches.

"Nobody will catch you," she continued, "because the children will only turn into mice hours later, when they are at school. Nobody will know that the sweets had the potion in them. The children will change. They will TURN INTO MICE!"

"What a horrible plan!" the witches shouted, happily.

"And what will happen next?" The Grand High Witch looked slowly around the room and the witches waited. "The teachers will put **mousetraps** around the school," she said. "The mice will eat the cheese in the traps, and SNAP! SNAP! The mice will die!"

At that moment, The Grand High Witch started to do a strange dance, and all the other witches joined her, laughing terribly.

Chapter 3 and Chapter 4
WHAT CAN YOU REMEMBER?

Write the correct words.

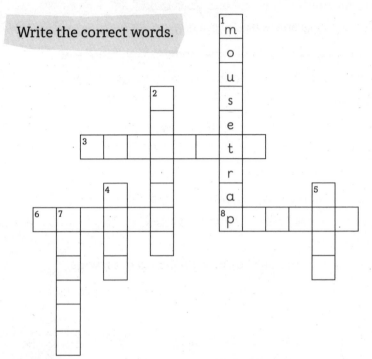

Down

1 This kills mice.

2 an important person in a business

4 You wear this over your face.

5 close a door with a key

7 a large flat thing. No one can see you behind it.

Across

3 become something different

6 run away from a bad place or person

8 a special drink that witches make

Put the sentences in the correct order.

| | The Grand High Witch describes her plan. |

| | The boy finds a large, empty hall and goes inside. |

| | Grandma becomes very ill. |

| | The witches take off their gloves, wigs and shoes. |

| 1 | The boy and his grandmother move to England. |

| | The boy plays with his mice behind a screen. |

| | A witch comes to the boy's garden. |

| | The boy and his grandmother go on holiday to Bournemouth. |

NEW WORDS

work (v.)

If something *works*,
it does what you want.

a drop (n. and v.)

a small amount of
water or drink

a bar (n.)

a flat piece of something

shrink *(shrank, shrunk)* (v.)

get smaller and smaller

fur, furry (n. and adj.)

hair on an animal's body

a paw (n.)

an animal's foot

Chapter 5 and Chapter 6
WHAT DO YOU THINK?

What will happen next in the story?
Answer the questions.

1 Look at the pictures on pages 42 and 43.
What is happening?

2 Look at the picture on page 44.
What can this witch smell?

3 Look at the picture on page 49.
Who is this mouse?

Now let's read Chapter 5 and Chapter 6!

CHAPTER 5
Bruno Jenkins disappears

I was still in the hall with the witches, watching them through the screen. I knew that I must not move or make any noise because then they would catch me.

The Grand High Witch started speaking again when, suddenly, one of the witches cried, "Look at those mice! Grand High Witch, you're so clever! You're wonderful! You've turned two children into mice!"

I saw that two mice were running around The Grand High Witch's skirt. But these were not The Grand High Witch's mice. They were mine! I recognized my own little William and Mary.

The Grand High Witch looked down at them, surprised. "Quiet!" she shouted to her witches. "I've never seen these mice before. They're not children. They're just normal mice, and I'm sure that a child in this hotel owns them!"

"Where's the child?" the other witches said. "We'll eat it for breakfast!"

"Be quiet!" shouted The Grand High Witch, angrily.

"The people at this hotel don't know that we're witches, so we must be careful."

"So how can we get rid of this horrible child?" they asked.

They're talking about me, I thought. *They're talking about how to kill me.*

"This child is not important," said The Grand High Witch. "I'll find him later and turn him into a fish, then eat him for dinner."

"Cut off his head!" cried the witches. "Cook him in hot butter!"

I was very frightened now. William and Mary were still running around near The Grand High Witch and, suddenly, she kicked William really hard. She did the same to Mary. They both hit the wall, but then they quickly ran away.

"Listen!" The Grand High Witch continued. "I'm going to show you that the potion **works**. Yesterday, I put one **drop** of the potion in a **bar** of chocolate and gave it to a horrible, smelly boy in the hotel. I asked him, *Was that nice? Do you want more?* He nodded, so I said, *Come to the hall tomorrow at half past three, and I'll give you six bars of chocolate.* He'll be here soon."

She was right. At that moment, somebody knocked on the doors and shouted, "Here I am! Give me my chocolate!"

"Quick!" cried The Grand High Witch. "The potion will work very soon! Put on your wigs! Put on your gloves! Put on your shoes!"

The witches quickly got ready, and The Grand High Witch put the mask back on. Suddenly, she became a pretty young woman again.

"Open the doors!" she said.

A witch opened the doors and a boy walked in. Then the witch locked the doors behind him again.

"I'm happy to see you again, my dear boy," said The Grand High Witch in a kind voice. "Your chocolate bars are here for you."

I recognized the boy. He was called Bruno Jenkins and he was staying at the hotel with his parents. His father had a big black moustache. I did not like Bruno. Every time

that I saw him, he was eating cake or crisps or chocolate.
And he kept saying, "My family is richer than yours! We
have three cars!" But I felt sad for him now, standing in
front of all those witches.

Bruno looked around the hall and did not understand.
He was not frightened, but he did not look comfortable.

"I want my chocolate," he said to The Grand High Witch.
But she did not give him the chocolate bars.

"It will work in ten seconds!" she cried to the witches. "Watch!"

"What are you talking about?" asked Bruno. "And where's my chocolate?"

At that moment, the potion in yesterday's chocolate started to work. Bruno's body began changing. The Grand High Witch jumped up and down happily. "This horrible, smelly boy will very soon be a mouse!" she cried.

Bruno was getting smaller. I could see him **shrinking**. He screamed! His clothes were disappearing and brown **fur** was growing on his body. Suddenly, he had a tail, and then he had four feet, and then Bruno was not there any more.

There was just a small brown mouse.

"That's wonderful! Well done!" shouted the witches.

The Grand High Witch took a mousetrap from her dress and put it on the floor. "Where is he?" she cried angrily.

Oh no! I thought. *I don't want to see this!*

But I did not need to worry because Bruno the mouse was already running away.

The Grand High Witch said, "He's gone, but it doesn't matter. Now, everyone sit down and listen."

CHAPTER 6
The potion

The Grand High Witch continued to the witches, "Before you leave the hotel, I will give you each a bottle of the potion."

"Oh, thank you, thank you!" said the witches.

She took out a small dark-blue glass bottle and showed it to them. "In this little bottle, there is enough potion to turn five hundred children into mice!"

The witches shouted, "Wow!"

Then The Grand High Witch said, "Now, we must go and have tea with that silly hotel manager, Mr Stringer. At six o'clock tonight, come to my room in small groups, and I'll give you the potion. My room is number 454. Then, at eight o'clock, we will meet for dinner. We will sit at two special long tables in the dining room. This meeting is now finished!"

The witches stood up. I was watching them through the screen. *Please hurry!* I thought. *Then I'll be safe again.*

"Wait!" shouted one of the witches at the back of the hall.

All the witches turned to look at her. "What is it?" they asked.

"I can smell dog poo!" she replied. "There's a child in this room!"

Then another witch said, "Yes, I can smell dog poo, too." Her huge nose holes got even wider.

Then all the witches put their noses in the air and they tried to smell the child. "She's right!" they said. "We can smell poo!"

"Find the child!" shouted The Grand High Witch. "Use your noses and find it!"

I was shaking, and all the hairs on my head stood up.

"It mustn't escape!" she continued. "If a child was here during the meeting, then it knows all our secrets. You must kill the child now!"

I can't escape! I thought. *There are a lot of witches in here and they'll easily catch me. What are they going to do to me?*

Then I turned around and saw a horrible face looking down at me. The face opened its mouth and shouted, happily, "It's here, behind the screen! Come and get the child!"

The witch reached out her hand and held me by my hair, but I escaped. I ran as fast as I could to the doors and tried to open them, but they were still locked.

Some of the witches held their noses and cried, "What a horrible smell of dog poo!"

"Catch him, you silly witches!" shouted The Grand High Witch. "Catch him!"

The witches moved slowly towards me. I began to scream. "Help!" I screamed. I hoped that somebody outside the hall could hear me. "Help! HELP!"

"Catch him!" shouted The Grand High Witch. "Stop him shouting!"

Five witches held me by my arms and legs. I screamed again, but one of them put her hand on my mouth and that stopped me.

"Bring him here!" shouted The Grand High Witch.

I was carried to the front of the hall. The witches were still holding me. Then I saw The Grand High Witch standing above me, smiling a horrible, frightening smile. She held up the bottle of potion and she said, "Now we'll give him some medicine! Hold his nose and he will open his mouth."

Strong fingers held my nose and, after a few moments, I had to open my mouth. As I did that, The Grand High Witch put the potion in my mouth. But she did not give me just one drop. She gave me all of it!

It really hurt! It burned me inside!

I screamed and screamed but, again, a hand went over my mouth. Then my skin started to feel strange. It was shrinking! *I* was shrinking! I felt mouse fur growing on my body.

The witches were laughing, and then I noticed that the floor was only 2 centimetres from my nose. I also noticed two furry **paws**, which I was able to move. They were mine!

I knew at that moment that I was not a boy any more. I was a mouse.

"Bring me the mousetrap and cheese!" shouted The Grand High Witch. But I ran as fast as I could. I jumped across witches' feet and ran between the chairs.

My mouse feet were fast, and I made no sound. I went behind a chair leg and stayed there.

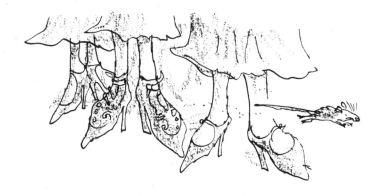

"Stop! You don't need to catch it," called The Grand High Witch. "It doesn't matter. It's only a mouse! Somebody else will soon catch it and kill it! Let's get out of here. The meeting is finished. Open the doors! We have to go and have tea with that stupid manager."

Chapter 5 and Chapter 6
WHAT CAN YOU REMEMBER?

Read the sentences and write the correct words.

paws	works	bar
shrinks	fur	drop

1 The Grand High Witch gives Bruno a
_____bar_____ of chocolate.

2 The Grand High Witch puts one _____
of the potion in the chocolate.

3 The Grand High Witch shows the witches that her
potion _____.

4 Bruno screams when he _____.

5 Brown _____ grows on Bruno's body.

6 The boy notices his furry _____.

Are these sentences true or false?
Correct the false sentences.

1   Bruno comes to the hall for cake.

False. Bruno comes to the hall for chocolate.

2   The Grand High Witch puts on her mask for
Bruno Jenkins.

_____

3   The Grand High Witch kills Bruno.

_____

4   The witches can smell the boy behind the screen.

_____

5   The witches give the boy one drop of potion.

_____

6   The witches catch the boy in a mousetrap.

_____

Chapter 7 and Chapter 8
NEW WORDS

peer (v.)
look around
something carefully

a floor (n.)
A building often
has many *floors*.

shocked (adj.)
very surprised about
a bad thing

a balcony (n.)
a place outside a high window
where you can stand

knitting (n.)
socks or a jumper that
you are making

a frog (n.)
a small green animal with
big eyes and two long legs

Chapter 7 and Chapter 8
WHAT DO YOU THINK?

What will happen next in the story?
Answer the questions.

1   Look at the picture on page 58.
Who is Grandma talking to?

2   Look at the picture on page 61.
What is Grandma doing with her knitting? Why?

3   Look at the pictures on page 62.
Where is the mouse? What is it holding?

Now let's read Chapter 7 and Chapter 8!

CHAPTER 7
Hello, Grandma

I **peered** around the leg of the chair and watched lots of witches' feet walking out of the hall. When I was alone again, I remembered Bruno.

"Bruno!" I called.

I did not think that I could talk any more because I was now a mouse. So I was surprised to hear my own voice. It was wonderful. My voice was as loud as when I was a boy. I was very pleased, so I spoke again. "Bruno Jenkins, where are you?"

There was no answer.

I decided that I was quite happy being a mouse. "Why?" you might ask. But I thought to myself, *It's not so great being a boy. Mice don't have to go to school. Mice don't have to do exams. They don't have to worry about money. It's true that mice are caught by people or by cats. But my grandmother will always love me, even if I'm a mouse, and she doesn't have a cat!*

I was walking around the hall, thinking about all of this,

when I saw another mouse. It was sitting on the
floor, eating a piece of bread that it was holding in
its front paws.

I was sure that it was Bruno. "Hello, Bruno," I said.
He looked up at me, then continued eating.

"What have you found?" I asked him.

"It's a sandwich. One of them dropped it," Bruno
answered. Hearing Bruno's loud voice coming out of a
small mouse was funny.

"Listen, Bruno," I said. "We're both mice now and we
have to start thinking about the future."

He stopped eating and looked at me with small black
eyes. "What do you mean *we*?" he asked. "*You're* a
mouse but that's not my problem."

"But you're a mouse, too, Bruno."

"Don't be silly," he replied. "I'm not a mouse."

"Of course you are, Bruno."

"I am not!" he shouted.

"The witches turned you into a mouse," I said. "Then they
did it to me, too."

"You're lying!" he cried. "I'm not a mouse!"

"You haven't noticed because you're too busy eating the sandwich," I said. "Look at your paws."

Bruno looked down at his paws. He jumped. "Oh no!" he cried. "I don't want to be a mouse! I'm Bruno Jenkins!"

"Being a mouse is fun," I told him. "You can live in a hole."

"I don't want to live in a hole!" Bruno shouted. "Which witch did this to me?"

"The witch who gave you the bar of chocolate yesterday," I answered. "Bruno, how will your parents feel about this, do you think?"

Bruno thought for a moment. "My father will be angry," he said, "and my mother's afraid of mice."

"Then you've got a problem, haven't you?"

"What about you?" he asked.

"My grandmother will understand," I replied. "She knows all about witches."

Bruno ate some more of his sandwich. "What shall we do?" he said.

"Let's go and speak to my grandmother," I said. "She'll know what to do." I took the sandwich from his paw and threw it on the floor. "Follow me."

I peered around the door of the hall. There was nobody there, so I ran as fast as I could, with Bruno following. We ran past the dining room and up the stairs. We stayed close to the wall because we did not want anyone to see us.

My grandmother's room was on the fifth **floor**. It took us a long time to get up there, but we were lucky because we did not meet anybody.

We stood outside her room and Bruno said, "How can we open the door?"

Suddenly, a hotel cleaner saw us, and she screamed loudly and ran away. My grandmother's door opened. "What's happening out here?" my grandmother said. I ran between her legs into her room, and Bruno followed me.

"Close the door, Grandma!" I cried.

Grandma looked down and saw two small mice on the floor. "Please hurry," I said, and this time she recognized my voice. Grandma was **shocked**. Her face became white, and she started to shake.

"Please close the door quickly, Grandma," I said. "The cleaner might come back."

She moved and closed the door, then she started crying.

"Don't cry, Grandma," I said. "I escaped from the witches. They didn't kill me."

Very slowly, she picked me up with one hand. Then she picked Bruno up with the other hand and put us both on the table. There was a bowl of bananas on the table and Bruno started eating one.

My grandmother sat down, still shocked.

"Oh, my dear boy," she said, crying again. "What have they done to you?"

"Don't worry, Grandma," I said. "It doesn't matter to me. I don't feel angry about it. I actually feel quite good. I know that you'll always look after me."

"Of course I will," my grandmother said.

"I'm not just a mouse," I said. "I can still think and talk like a boy."

"You're a mouse-person," said my grandmother, "and you're very special. Now, who's the other mouse?"

"That's a boy called Bruno Jenkins," I told her.

"And where's the witch now?" she asked.

"Grandma," I said, "there isn't just one witch. There are nearly a hundred of them in this hotel!"

She looked at me. She could not believe it. "Do you mean that they had their secret meeting here?"

"Yes, Grandma!" I said. "And The Grand High Witch is here, too."

Suddenly, my grandmother looked excited. "Tell me everything."

And I did.

CHAPTER 8
Stealing the bottle

After I finished telling Grandma my story, I said, "We've got to stop them, Grandma. They want to turn all the children in England into mice."

"You can't stop witches," she replied. She touched my fur, which felt nice. "They can kill all of us."

"I've got a plan," I said.

"What is it, my dear?"

"The Grand High Witch's room is number 454. And my room number is 554. Mine is on the fifth floor and hers is on the fourth floor. So room 454 is under room 554, is that right?"

"That's correct," my grandmother answered.

"Would you please take me on to my **balcony**? I want to look down," I said. All the rooms in the Hotel Magnificent had private balconies. My grandmother carried me through my own bedroom and on to my balcony. We both looked down to the balcony below.

"The witches are having tea with Mr Stringer," I said.

"So The Grand High Witch isn't in her room. She'll come back to her room at six o'clock because, at that time, the other witches are coming to get the potion. I can go into her room from her balcony, I'm sure," I continued. "And look, the door to her balcony is open!"

"I won't allow this," my grandmother cried. "It's too dangerous! And why do you want to get into her room?"

"I can find a bottle of the potion and bring it back here."

"But what will you do with it?" my grandmother asked.

"One bottle is enough for five hundred people," I said. "We can use it to turn all the witches into mice."

My grandmother jumped into the air. "That's a great plan!" she cried. "We would get rid of every witch in England *and* The Grand High Witch!"

"But how can I get on to the balcony?" I asked.

"I have an idea," said my grandmother. She put me inside her **knitting**. "You can go down to the witch's balcony in this," she said. "But we must hurry! That horrible woman will come back to her room soon! Are you ready?"

"I hope that I can do this," I said, feeling a little afraid. "I'm only a mouse."

"You can do it!" she said. My grandmother held one end of the knitting and dropped it slowly down towards the balcony, with me inside.

I peered out, and when I got to The Grand High Witch's

balcony, I jumped out of the knitting and ran into the room. I heard my grandmother shouting, "Hurry! Hurry!"

Suddenly, I saw a **frog** jumping across the room and under the bed. I jumped, too, from surprise.

I heard my grandmother again. "Get the potion and leave!"

I looked all around the room for the potion, but it was not there. Then I thought about the bed. I quickly ran under it. Yes! Under the bed there were lots of small dark blue glass bottles, and I took one. On the bottle, it said, *Mouse-maker (This potion turns 500 people into mice).*

There were three frogs under the bed, too. They looked at me with large black eyes. They looked so sad. "Were you children, too?" I asked.

At that moment, I heard a key in the door and the door opened. The Grand High Witch came into the room. I ran behind the leg of the bed, holding the bottle. Suddenly, The Grand High Witch's face peered under the bed. She was wearing her mask.

"Here you are, my little frogs," she said. "I'm going to throw you out of the window. Then the birds can eat you for dinner."

But then I heard my grandmother's loud voice through the open balcony door. "Hurry up, my dear!"

"Who's calling?" said The Grand High Witch, angrily. I peered from behind the leg of the bed and saw her walking towards the balcony. "Why is there knitting here?" she said.

"Oh, hello," came my grandmother's voice. "I just dropped my knitting on to your balcony by mistake. I'm sorry. I can pull it up again."

"Who were you talking to?" asked The Grand High Witch.

"I was talking to my little grandson," my grandmother answered. "He's been in the bathroom for hours! He sits in there reading books and forgets the time. Do you have any children, my dear?"

"I do not!" shouted The Grand High Witch, closing the balcony door and quickly coming back into the bedroom.

Oh no! I thought. *How can I escape now? If she sees me, she'll throw me to the birds too.*

Then somebody knocked on the bedroom door. It was the first group of witches, who were coming for their bottles of potion.

Chapter 7 and Chapter 8
WHAT CAN YOU REMEMBER?

Look at the letters and write the words.

1   **eepr**

p   e   e   r

2   **grof**

___ ___ ___ ___

3   **gtkninit**

___ ___ ___ ___ ___ ___ ___ ___

4   **oalybcn**

___ ___ ___ ___ ___ ___ ___

5   **frool**

___ ___ ___ ___

6   **doscehk**

___ ___ ___ ___ ___ ___ ___

List the good and bad things about being a mouse.
Use the words in the box.

school   afraid   money

cats   exams   people

mousetrap   worry

Good things

1   Mice don't have to go to school.

2   _____

3   _____

Bad things

1   _____

2   _____

3   _____

Chapter 9 and Chapter 10
NEW WORDS

a cook (n.)

someone who cooks
food in a restaurant

hide (hid) (v.)

If you *hide*, people
can't find you.

swing (swung) (v.)

hold something high and move
your body from side to side

whisper (v.)

speak very quietly

a shelf (shelves) (n.)

A *shelf* is on the wall.
You put things on it.

a handle (n.)

You use the *handle*
on a door to open it.

pour (v.)

put water or a drink
into something

Chapter 9 and Chapter 10
WHAT DO YOU THINK?

What will happen next in the story?
Answer the questions.

1   Look at the picture on page 72.
Where is this? Who are these people?

2   Look at the pictures on page 73.
Where is the mouse? What is he doing?

3   Look at the picture on page 76.
What is happening to the witches?

Now let's read Chapter 9 and Chapter 10!

CHAPTER 9
In the kitchen

The Grand High Witch walked across her hotel bedroom and opened the door. "Come in!" she said. She was still angry with my grandmother. I saw some shoes entering the room.

I ran towards the door. I jumped over a lot of pairs of shoes and, in three seconds, I was outside the room, still holding the bottle. There were no shouts of *Mouse! Mouse!* I was lucky.

I ran up to my bedroom and quietly knocked on the door with the bottle. But the door did not open, so I shouted, as loudly as I could, "Grandma!"

The door opened and I ran in, crying, "Look, Grandma! I've got a bottle of potion!"

My grandmother closed the door, and picked me up. "That's wonderful, and I'm so pleased that you're safe."

My grandmother remembered Bruno. He was still in the banana bowl on the table. "You've already eaten three bananas!" she said to him.

Then she looked at me. "We've got the potion, but how are we going to put it into the witches' food?"

"They're having dinner in the dining room at eight o'clock," I answered.

"It's now seven o'clock," she said, "so we've got an hour."

"I have a plan," I said. "Because mice are so small, we can go to places that people can't. I'll go into the kitchen, where the witches' food is made, and put the potion into their meals."

"That's a great idea!" my grandmother cried. "You're a very clever mouse! But it's going to be very dangerous. Nobody wants a mouse in the kitchen. If the **cooks** see you, they'll kill you, so you must **hide**."

"They won't see me," I answered.

"You're so brave," she said. "I'll go down to dinner and

take you into the dining room in my bag."

"What shall we do with Bruno?" I asked.

Bruno looked up. "I'm coming with you," he said, speaking with his mouth full of banana. "I'm not going to miss my dinner!"

"Yes, all right," said my grandmother. "I'll keep you in my handbag and give you some food." Then she said to me, "Would you like something to eat, my dear?"

"No, thank you," I said. "I can't eat because I'm so excited. I've got important work to do."

"That's right," my grandmother said. "This is the biggest job that you'll ever do."

Soon it was half past seven. "OK, let's go!" my grandmother said. She picked Bruno up and put him in her handbag. Then she kissed me on the nose and put me in her bag, too, with the little bottle. "Don't forget that you have a tail now," she said to me. "It might be useful in the kitchen. You can put it around things and **swing** from it."

"Yes, you're right, Grandma," I said, happily.

She walked downstairs with us and we reached the dining room. It was huge, and lots of people were already eating. Waiters were hurrying everywhere, carrying plates and glasses. Our table was a small one against a wall. My grandmother sat down at the table.

Peering out of the handbag, I could see two long tables that were still empty.

My grandmother **whispered** to me in the handbag. "I'm going to put you on the floor under the table. Have you got the bottle?"

"Yes, Grandma. I'm ready," I said.

She slowly put me on the floor and whispered, "Go, my dear, go!"

I stood with the bottle in my front paws. I could see the door to the kitchen and started running around the walls of the dining room towards it.

I ran. I ran fast!

I was nearly at the kitchen door when a huge group of people entered the dining room. I pressed myself against the wall, holding the bottle. First, I only saw the shoes of

the women who were coming into the room. But then
I looked up and I knew who they were. They were the
witches coming in for dinner!

I waited while they all passed me and then I hurried to
the kitchen door. A waiter opened it and I ran in after him.
The kitchen was so noisy and busy! And all the
cooks were shouting!

The waiters hurried in and out,
screaming food orders to the
cooks. A waiter came in and
shouted, "Everyone on the two
big tables wants the soup!"

I started listening very
carefully now. I was hiding
behind a box of food and
I peered around the side of
it. A cook shouted, "Put the
soup for the group into the
largest bowl!"

That's where I'll put the potion,
I thought. I noticed that there was a **shelf** above the bowl.
*I have to climb up there, but how can I do that? And first,
I have to go across the kitchen.*

Then I remembered my wonderful tail! I jumped up and
put the end of my tail around a **handle** on a cupboard.

Then I began to swing, higher and higher.

At the right moment, I took my tail off the handle and flew across the kitchen and fell onto the shelf.

No one saw me. They were all too busy. I moved along the shelf until I was above the large bowl. Then I took the top off the bottle and **poured** the potion into the bowl below me.

Moments later, a cook brought the soup and poured it into that same bowl. Then a waiter carried the bowl into the dining room.

I've done it! I thought.

I left the empty bottle on the shelf and, swinging from lots of different handles, I moved across the kitchen. *This is fun!* I thought.

Suddenly, a man's voice screamed, "There's a mouse, a dirty little mouse!" I saw a knife fly past me and it cut off the end of my tail!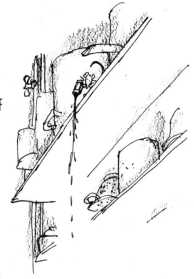

I fell to the floor and ran as fast as I could.

"Kill it!" everyone shouted, and I saw big black boots all around me.

CHAPTER 10
Mice everywhere

But I was lucky. I found a big bag of potatoes and I hid in there, and the cooks soon forgot about me. My tail was really hurting, but when a waiter opened the door into the dining room, I hurried through it.

I could see my grandmother's feet and I climbed up one of her legs. "Hello, Grandma!" I whispered. "I did it! I poured all the potion into their soup!"

"Well done!" she whispered back. "And look, they're eating the soup now! But what happened to your poor tail? Don't worry, I'll help you!" She put me into her handbag and I watched the witches safely from there.

Bruno was in the handbag, too. "Your grandmother gave me some nice bread," he said.

At that moment, I saw a man with a big black moustache walking towards us. "Here comes Bruno's father, Grandma!" I whispered.

Mr Jenkins arrived at our table, looking very angry.

"Where is your grandson?" he said to my grandmother.

"I can't find my son and I think that our two boys are together, doing something naughty. Bruno never misses his dinner! Do you know where he's hiding?"

"Your son has turned into a mouse," my grandmother answered.

"What are you talking about?" shouted Mr Jenkins. "My son isn't a mouse!" His black moustache jumped up and down as he spoke.

"Bruno *is* a mouse," my grandmother said, quietly.

"No, he isn't!" shouted Mr Jenkins.

"Oh, yes, I am!" Bruno said, peering out of the handbag.

Mr Jenkins jumped about a metre into the air.

"Hello, Dad," Bruno said.

"Mrs Jenkins will be very angry," cried Mr Jenkins. "She hates mice! How did this happen?"

"A witch did it," my grandmother said. Then, with a naughty smile on her face, she pointed to The Grand High Witch and said, "That one did it."

"But she isn't a witch!" cried Mr Jenkins.

Suddenly, there was a loud scream and I saw that The Grand High Witch was standing on her chair! Now she was on top of the table, waving her arms and still screaming. Then all the other witches began to scream and jump up, too! Then, suddenly, they became quiet. Everyone in the dining room watched them. They were shocked.

"They're shrinking, Grandma!" I said. "They're shrinking like I did!"

"Yes, that's right," my grandmother said.

In a few more seconds, all the witches disappeared, and the tops of the two long tables were full of small brown mice.

All around the dining room, people were screaming and waiters were hitting the mice with chairs. A cook ran out of the kitchen, shouting, "Mice! Mice! We must get rid of the mice!"

"We should go now," my grandmother said to me. She stood up and she put Bruno into Mr Jenkins's hand. "Here's your little boy," she said.

Then my grandmother, with me in her handbag, turned and walked through the dining room and out of the hotel. Outside, it was a lovely warm evening and I could hear the waves on the beach.

My grandmother called a taxi and we got in. "Take us to the station, please," my grandmother told the driver.

"Are we going home?" I asked her.

"Yes," she answered. "We're going back to Norway."

"Yes!" I cried. "Hurrah!"

My grandmother held me in her hands and said, "We did great work today."

"It was wonderful," I said.

Chapter 9 and Chapter 10
WHAT CAN YOU REMEMBER?

Read the sentences and write the correct words.

> handle   pours   ~~whispers~~
>
> shelf   swing   cooks   hides

1   Grandma   _whispers_   advice to the mouse in her handbag.

2   There are lots of waiters and _____ working in the kitchen.

3   The mouse puts his tail around a _____.

4   He begins to _____ higher and higher.

5   Then he flies across the kitchen to the _____ above the bowl.

6   He _____ the potion into the bowl.

7   The mouse _____ in a big bag of potatoes.

1   The mice hide in Grandma's **suitcase**.

The mice hide in Grandma's **handbag**.

2   The kitchen is quiet and empty.

_____

3   The potion is in the witches' salad.

_____

4   A knife cuts off the end of the mouse's nose.

_____

5   Mrs Jenkins will be very pleased that her son is a mouse.

_____

6   The witches start getting bigger.

_____

NEW WORDS

a gadget (n.)

a small machine

a ladder (n.)

You climb a *ladder*
to get to a high place.

tiny (adj.)

very small

perfect (adj.)

very good in every way

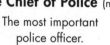

the Chief of Police (n.)

The most important
police officer.

a recipe (n.)

A *recipe* usually tells you how
to make a cake or a meal.

Chapter 11 and Chapter 12
WHAT DO YOU THINK?

What will happen next in the story?
Answer the questions.

1 Look at the picture on page 82.
Where is the mouse?

2 Look at the picture on page 88.
What is the mouse doing? How is he feeling?

3 Look at the picture on page 91.
Does the story have a happy end or a sad end,
do you think?

Now let's read Chapter 11 and Chapter 12!

CHAPTER 11
A mouse's life

I loved being back in Norway again, in my grandmother's beautiful old house. But I was really small, and moving around the house was difficult. I could not open doors or reach things that were on tables.

After a few days, my grandmother began making **gadgets** to make my life easier. There was a gadget that I could press with my paw to open the doors. There was a gadget to help me turn on the lights. And she even made a tall, thin **ladder** for me to climb to the top of the table.

My grandmother made me a **tiny** toothbrush, too. I could not use a big bath, so I used a sugar bowl and I had a bath in it every night before going to bed.

My grandmother allowed nobody else into the house. We were alone and happy to be together.

One evening, I was sitting with my grandmother in front of the fire.

"Can I ask you something, Grandma?" I said.

"Of course you can, my dear."

"How long does a mouse live?" I asked.

She was silent for a while.

"Grandma, why don't you tell me?" I asked. I was a bit worried.

"I'm sorry," she said, "but mice don't live for a long time. They only live for about three years. But you're not a normal mouse. You're a mouse-person."

"And how long do mouse-people live?" I asked.

"About nine years," my grandmother replied.

"That's great!" I cried. "That's the best news that I've ever heard!"

"Why do you say that?" she asked. She was surprised.

"I don't want to live longer than you," I said. "I don't want anyone else to look after me. How old are you, Grandma?"

"I'm eighty-six," she answered.

"Will you live for another eight or nine years?"

"I might," she said.

"You have to," I said, "because then I'll be a very old

mouse and you'll be a very old grandmother. And, soon after that, we'll die together."

"That sounds **perfect**," she said. "But are you sure that you aren't sad about being a mouse?"

"I'm not sad," I said. "It doesn't matter who you are if somebody loves you."

CHAPTER 12
Our biggest job

That evening, I ran up the ladder to the top of the table, and my grandmother and I had dinner together. My grandmother had eggs and bread, and I had some cheese on a small plate.

"Grandma," I said, "we've got rid of The Grand High Witch, so will all the other witches in the world disappear now, too?"

"No, I'm sure that they won't," she answered.

"But who will give them orders and speak at the meetings, and who will make their potions now?" I asked.

"When one Grand High Witch dies, another one takes her job," my grandmother said.

"Oh no!" I cried. "What we did in the hotel didn't help!"

"We saved all the children of England!" she said.

"I know, I know!" I cried. "But that's not good enough! There are still hundreds of other witches in the world!"

There was a secret smile on my grandmother's face.

"Why are you smiling, Grandma?" I asked her.

"I have some interesting news for you," she replied.

"What is it?" I asked.

"When we arrived back in Norway," she said, "I phoned the **Chief of Police** in Bournemouth. I told him, *I am the Chief of Police in Norway.*"

"Did he believe you?" I asked. I was surprised.

"Of course he did," she answered. "I asked him for the name and address of the woman from Room 454 in the Hotel Magnificent."

"You mean The Grand High Witch!" I cried.

"Yes, my dear."

"And did he give it to you?"

"Of course. The Chief of Police always helps another Chief of Police."

"You're very naughty, Grandma!" I said, smiling. "Where did she live? Tell me."

"Her home was a castle," my grandmother continued.

"Where's the castle, Grandma?" I cried. "Tell me now!"

"Guess," she said.

"It's in Norway!" I shouted.

"That's right!" she answered. "It's high up in the mountains above a small village. The *new* Grand High Witch lives in that castle now, with lots of other witches. And inside that castle, there are also the names and addresses of every witch in the world!"

This was exciting news. I did a little dance on the table.

"We have work to do, you and I," cried my grandmother. "It's great that you're a tiny mouse! A tiny mouse can go anywhere! A tiny mouse can easily hide! You'll be able to get inside The Grand High Witch's castle and look around."

"I will! I will!" I answered. "No one will ever see me!"

"Your most important job will be to get rid of every witch in the castle," she said.

"How can I do that?" I cried.

"Can't you guess?" she asked.

"Tell me," I said.

"Mouse-maker potion!" she shouted. "But do you know the **recipe**?"

"Yes, I do!" I answered. "The recipe was written on the bottle, and I remember it! Do you mean that we're going to make the potion ourselves?"

"Why not?" cried my grandmother.

"What will happen when all the witches become mice?" I asked.

"Then the castle will be empty," said my grandmother, "and I'll come and join you."

"Wait!" I cried. "I've just had a terrible thought!"

"What is it?" she said.

"When the potion turned *me* into a mouse," I said, "I didn't become a normal mouse. I became a clever mouse who is very difficult to catch!"

My grandmother was silent. She understood the problem.

"If we use the potion to turn the *new* Grand High Witch and all the other witches into mice," I continued, "the castle will be full of horrible mouse-witches! It will be really dangerous!"

"You're right," she answered. "I never thought of that!"

"How can I get rid of all the mouse-witches?" I said.

"You can't," she replied, "and I can't either. They will be clever mice and we won't be able to catch them using mousetraps. And there are no cooks to kill the mice with their kitchen knives, like in the Hotel Magnificent."

I thought for a moment, then shouted, "I've got the answer!"

"Tell me!" my grandmother said.

"The answer is CATS!" I shouted.

My grandmother looked at me. There was a huge smile on her face and she cried, "That's a great idea! It's perfect!"

"We'll put lots of cats into the castle and they'll kill all the mouse-witches!" I said.

"You're wonderful!" my grandmother shouted, happily, waving her arms in the air. "They may be clever mice, but a cat can still catch them."

"What will we do when all the mice are dead?" I asked her.

"You and I will live in the castle alone," she replied. "And we'll find the names and addresses of all the witches in the world!"

"And what will happen then?" I asked, shaking excitedly.

"After that, my dear, our biggest job will begin!" she said. "We will go travelling all around the world! In every country, we will find the witches' houses. You'll go inside and put a drop of potion into the witch's bread or soup. And we'll do it together, just you and me! That will be our job for all our lives!"

My grandmother picked me up from the table and kissed me on the nose. "We're going to be very busy!" she cried.

"Yes, we are," I said. "It's going to be a lot of fun!"

"Yes, it will," my grandmother agreed.

"I can't wait to start!" I said.

WHAT CAN YOU REMEMBER?

Find the words or phrases and write them down.

Moladderptiperfectwtinyrecigadgetnorwrecipezhrichiefofpolicecactc

1 _____ladder_____   4 _____

2 _____   5 _____

3 _____   6 _____

Match the two parts of the sentences.

1   Grandma makes . . .   <u>d</u>

2   The mouse washes . . .   _____

3   Mice do not live . . .   _____

4   The Chief of Police gives Grandma . . . _____

5   The recipe was written . . .   _____

6   Lots of cats will kill . . .   _____

a   . . . the address of the castle.

b   . . . all the mouse-witches.

c   . . . in a sugar bowl every night.

d   . . . lots of gadgets.

e   . . . on the bottle of potion.

f   . . . for a long time.

TALK ABOUT . . .

Ask and answer the questions with your friend.

1 Did you enjoy the story?

Yes! I enjoyed the story because . . .

2 Who is your favourite person or animal in the story? Why?

3 What was the most frightening part of the story, do you think? Why?

4 Can the boy and his grandmother kill all the witches, do you think? Is their plan a good one?

5 Would you enjoy being a mouse, or a different animal? Why / Why not?

6 How many new words did you learn?

PROJECT!

There are lots of different stories about witches.
Answer these questions. You can use books or the
internet, or watch films or TV.

1 Choose a witch from a different book,
film or TV show.

2 What is the witch called?

3 What do they look like?

4 Is the witch good, bad or both?

5 What can the witch do? Can they fly?
Can they turn people into animals?

6 Do people in the story fight the witch? How?

Now make a **poster** about a witch in a different
story. You can draw pictures, or use photos from the
internet, too!

ROALD DAHL

Penguin Readers

Some projects involve research **online**. Remember: ensure an adult is supervising; use established search engines such as Google or Kiddle; and never share personal details such as your name, home or school address, telephone number or photos.